TECHNOLOGY FOR ART IN EUROPE

PERKIN ELMER

Acknowledgments
The author and publisher would like to express their sincere thanks to the following persons:
Mauro Matteini and Giancarlo Lanterna, Opificio delle Pietre Dure, Florence; Marcello Miccio,
Soprintendenza ai Beni Archeologici della Toscana, Centro di Restauro, Florence; Mauro Bacci,
Istituto di Ricerca sulle Onde Elettromagnetiche, C.N.R., Florence; Piero Frediani, Centro di
Studio delle Cause di Deperimento e dei Metodi di Conservazione delle Opere d'Arte, C.N.R.,
Florence; Walter Persegati and Nazzareno Gabrielli, Monumenti Musei e Gallerie Pontificie,
Vatican City; Giovanna Alessandrini and Roberto Bugini, Centro "Gino Bozza" per lo Studio
delle Cause di Deperimento e dei Metodi di Conservazione delle Opere d'Arte, C.N.R., Milan;
Iulia Vokotopoulou, Museum of Thessalonike; Manolis Andronicos, University of Thessalonike;
Claire Chahine, Centre de Recherches sur la Conservation des Documents Graphiques, Paris;
Juliette Hours, Laboratoire de Recherche des Musées de France, Louvre, Paris; Nicole Meyer,
Unité d'Archéologie, Saint-Denis (Paris);
Maria Karreman, Rijksmuseum, Amsterdam;
the colleagues Gérard Garrabé, Perkin-Elmer France; Giovanni Petrucci and Francisco Farré,
Perkin-Elmer Hispania; Eduard Pieper, Perkin-Elmer Switzerland; Tony Hardware, Perkin-
Elmer England; Jos van Dijk, Perkin-Elmer Holland; Raniero Goracci, Perkin-Elmer Italiana
Florence; Sergio Gallo and Pietro Gambero, Perkin-Elmer Italiana Rome.
A special acknowledgment to Bob Davis, Perkin-Elmer Marketing Support, and Jutta Mosinski,
Perkin-Elmer GmbH Ueberlingen, for the revision of the English text and for the translation into
German.

Acknowledgments for photographs:
The author and publisher would like to express their sincere thanks to the following institutions
for granting permission to reproduce the photographs used in this volume:
Nicolas Picoulas, Ministry of Culture, Archaeological Receipts Fund (TAP Service), Athens;
NTV-Tokyo and Vatican Museums, Vatican City; The Master and Fellows of Magdalene
College, Cambridge; Unité d'Archéologie of Saint-Denis (Paris); Rijksmuseum of Amsterdam.

Published by the Marketing Center, Perkin-Elmer Europe
Project, editing and art direction: Martina Luciani
Project coordinator: Carlo Piccinini

Printed and bound in Italy by: Amilcare Pizzi S.p.A. Arti Grafiche,
Cinisello Balsamo (Milan)
Layout: Guido Modena

Cover/jacket: analytical instrumentation on the background of the vault of Mantegna's
"Chamber of the Married Couple", Palazzo Ducale, Mantova, Italy.

INTRODUCTION

The original idea of this book was to provide pleasant and interesting reading, while presenting Perkin-Elmer from a point of view completely different from its normal scientific and technological identity.

The project was oriented towards that area of research and activity which foresees scientists and technicians engaged in the study of restoration of works of art. From the first steps of investigation and gathering of editorial material we become more deeply involved than we had imagined we would be. We went through centuries and centuries of testimonies of sentiment, imagination, and different cultural identities along the roads of science and culture. We experienced emotion and astonishment where similarly the adventures of mankind march restlessly on. A boundless journey, it could have required an editorial encyclopaedia. Therefore we were obliged to limit it in two ways. First of all in area. We restricted research, in a geographical sense, concentrating it on the artistic patrimony of Europe and to a few examples, very famous but also less well known, in the fields of painting, architecture, sculpture and archaeology. Secondly in the concept by giving priority in the choice of topics to those works of conservation and of restoration which highlighted the application of different analytical and instrumental techniques.

We believe that the result is extremely significant. First of all, it is a recognition of the merits of those who work in this field with scientific accuracy and passion. They contribute, side by side with philologists and historians, to the preservation of the creations of art and of human genius for future generations.

It also provides an opportunity to reflect on how the concepts and techniques of restoration have evolved over the last few years by introducing and developing the phenomena of a true and meaningful relationship between the most sophisticated technologies of scientific analysis and the message of a work of art. Two worlds so far apart have found the way to meet. The first at the service of the second and the second ever more in need of the sophisticated control and care which the first can guarantee and indicate.

Finally this journey allows us to emphasize a further relationship. We decided to dedicate this book to the initiative for preservation and restoration in the field of art that is being taken in several European countries in order to underline the European

5

dimension of Perkin-Elmer. The company has two production factories and three centres for research and development of analytical equipment. They are in Beaconsfield (U.K.), Ueberlingen and Oberschleissheim (West Germany). Over five hundred technicians spread over 80 offices guarantee assistance and highly-qualified support to all users of Perkin-Elmer instruments.

In conclusion, we believe that we have selected a varied but coherent group of subjects well worth considering. We offer a text which we trust will be pleasant to read from the aesthetic point of view, while being stimulating in its contents, and capable of communicating the same enthusiasm that we felt when we approached the world of restoration and preservation of our artistic wealth.

Antonio Portolan

General Manager
Sales and Service Sector,
Europe, Middle East, West Asia, Africa,
Latin America, Caribbean

FROM THE AUTHOR

This book is a particular initiative outside the customary publishing activities of Perkin-Elmer. The company is normally concerned with scientific problems, analytical methodology and technical development. This is not due so much because of the subjects chosen, which are closely connected to the research and the productivity of Perkin-Elmer, but rather because of the type of approach and the interpretation of the subjects dealt with.

Planning of such an undertaking as "Technology for Art in Europe" could possibly have been characterized by the many and diverse documentary, historical scientific and journalistic points of view or writings, but the final result would probably not have allowed for precise reference to anyone of these sources. On the other hand the study of documents, historical research, academic reference, scientific reports and journalistic investigations were instrumental in the lengthy preparatory work for this book.

Using these sources, we have tried to create a sensation of reappraisal of the facts, the concepts and the sensations which have already had distinguished interpretations and observations. Without presuming to have discovered anything new, we have tried to find new wavelengths for a relationship with a painting, a fresco, an archaeological exhibit and with the phenomena of art in general. We are not proposing alternative interpretations to those already made and accepted, but want to promote reactions and a little meditation. Our emphasis is on something which has more to do with sentiment and poetry than art criticism. Our attention is turned more to the mysterious throbs that art can communicate than to historical truth. Our book attempts this, with simplicity and respect. With affection, too, for man, for his desire for beauty, with his aspiration to seek out and communicate with shapes and words that purity which is inside and outside each of us and which frees us from our mental and physical limitations. For these reasons we must be forgiven if, amongst reality and fantasy, the greatness of universal works and personalities, the complexities of historical events, the experience of civilization and nations and the identities of populations and individuals, we have been restrained by the limits of our thoughts and by subjective judgement.

Martina Luciani

8   Santo Domingo, the Abbey.

ELVES, HEROES, KINGS:
SPAIN BETWEEN POETRY AND HISTORY

Sculptured, decorated, softened by sinuous curves, strong and square, tapering towards the top, smoothed and rounded, the stones of the Spanish monuments have so many shapes, embody so many stories, evoke so many memories. And there amidst the mighty embattled rampants, the exuberant buildings of picturesque art, the Moorish domes, the medieval abbeys, the rich façades of the churrigueresque baroque, the polished marble columns and the gleam of the mosaics, is the "duende", the Spanish elf. This is the elf who possesses and discloses the magic inspiration of poetry. Hidden away, at times he reveals himself or comes into contact with the sensitive minds and hearts, in a harmony of beauty, intensity and sentiment. The duende is unlike any other being of the great nation of fairies and dwarfs: the duende is a son of Spain. He has the dark and flashing eyes of an Arab horseman, the frank and loyal face of a Roman leader, the swift moves of a gypsy flamenco dancer, the brave impulse of a paladine, the idealistic nobility of Don Quixote, the charisma of Cid Campeador, the audacity of a toreador in the arena. The duende certainly knows the country. Like an acrobat, he vaults from one to another of the fantastic borders which define the Spanish world, miraculously joining together their different cultures and traditions which form the kaleidoscope of Iberian identity. Not by ways of numerous fossilized strata, but through a vivacious blend of different characters, features, styles, thoughts: Phoenician, Greek, Roman, barbaric invaders, Islam, Christianity, Romanesque, French gothic, Flemish art, European Renaissance and so on. The air resounds with the verses of the Arab poets, the reverberation of the Gregorian chant, the rhymes of the chivalric poetry, the exotic echoes of Moslem music, the rhythm of the catholic prayers. The result is moving, unique and characteristic. It is Spain, on the way to the West Indies, way beyond the seas of mystery and courage and the mythical Catai towards which Angelica and Melidoro sailed from the port of Barcellona.

SPAIN

Along the roads of Spain the pilgrims of all times could meet the most fascinating and strangest figures including saints and bandits, wise and exuberant common people, "hidalgos" and fascinating black-haired girls. They could recognize among the noisy crowds of the cities, the Alcaide first in the clothes of a Moslem judge, or then centuries later, in those of the highest town authority. They had to hide from the black looks of the Inquisitor. They had rested in the claustral quiet of a Benedictine monastery. They were cheered by the unrestrained joy of a "fiesta" and fascinated by the violent emotions of a bullfight.

Stories of men and events that read like a great novel are in the endless architectural testimony scattered everywhere. Spain is all memories and romances. It is made up of mosques and abbeys, castles and walls, of roads, squares and palaces surrounded by natural scenery which ponders on the meaning of such stories. For example Castile, the geographical and ideal heart of the country is enclosed in the mountains. As such it is always compelled to suffer torrid summers and then windy, freezing winters. Living in such a difficult land has molded the character of its hard-headed, strong and proud people. Destiny made up for the rest. The people of Castile with their war-like spirit, their weapons and their courage were given the task of founding the Spanish nation. From the year 1000 to 1400 Burgos was the capital of Old Castile where the Spanish national hero Ruy Diaz de Vivar was born in 1026. Using the name Cid Campeador, he has entered the Olympus of great leaders.

Poets and artists drew inspiration from him to highlight the image of a Medieval knight, of a warrior both somewhat mystical and something of an adventurer, ever strong and courageous. They created a leading character for the romantic and heroic spirit which enlivened the fight to reconquer the country from the Arabs.

El Cid is buried in the magnificent cathedral of the town. The temple is one of the most remarkable examples of gothic architecture in Spain. It is austere and reflects the stern Castilian religion.

Queen Isabella was called "the Catholic" since she supported the dreaded organization of the Inquisition while emphasizing the viewpoint that it was an instrument of control at the service of the monarchy. The past constructive experiences of coexistence among Christians, Arabs and Jews were thrown to the wind. The rule became "those who do not belong to the Church do not belong to the State".

It is also true that Isabella supported Cristoforo Colombo's plan even though there were thousands of reasons for considering that the voyage of the Genoan was futile madness. Her support promoted the opening of a fundamental chapter in Spanish history.

Near Burgos is Santo Domingo de Silos, a Benedictine abbey which was founded in 919. The large complex of the monastery conserves many treasures of Spanish art. Like so many others in the rest of Europe, it played a primary role in both the religious area and in the cultural and social fields during the so-called "dark ages". The romanesque cloister with two orders of columns is one of the most elegant in Spain and dates back to the 11th century. The precious series of decorated capitals shows the tendency, both in style and history, of combining elements of Christian and Moslem art. This was called "moresque" and is a unique expression of the Spanish medieval period. Ancient manuscripts containing evidence and data of inestimable value are contained within the heart of the abbey. They document, amongst other things, the linguistic origins of the Castilian language of this area.

In the highlands in Old Castile at more than a thousand meters above sea level stands Segovia. Here the famous and enormous Roman aqueduct is still in use and here there are still many buildings showing the Arab influence.

Here also is found the towering castle Alcazar which was the wedding residence of Isabella of Castile and Ferdinand of Aragon. Performed in 1469, this was no ordinary wedding. A papal bull was needed to authorize the wedding of the two cousins and the marriage partners were each sovereigns of two important realms. But more importantly, this festive day is considered as the moment in history when the destinies of a gravely-divided country were eventually reunited thus establishing the basis for the final reconquest of the last of the Arab sheikdoms in Andalusia. Isabella and Ferdinand each maintained their sovereign power over their own country. He in Aragon as the only heir of his father John II while she as Queen of Castile continued to administer the country. She shared with her husband only questions regarding justice, the signature of royal letters and the minting of coins which bore both their images. They consolidated the monarchy while strengthening their power over the country. This formed the basis for the rapid growth of the new Spain. They overcame the difficulties of reuniting those who had quarrelled and the consequences of social and monastic conflicts which had tormented the previous period.

The unification of the country had remarkable effects in Spain and in Europe, especially with the defeat of the Arabs. In 1480 Isabella and Ferdinand began operations of war. One-by-one they conquered the castles of the Sierra Nevada and in 1492 had arrived at Granada which was the last stronghold of the Moorish resistance. The Arabs had entered Spain through Gibraltar 781 years before in 711.

Oddly enough, the tombs of the royal couple are actually in Granada. Here the Alhambra, that refined and fabulous royal palace, is an astonishing and precious testimony of the Arab wealth, taste and wisdom.

West of Castile in the district of León, is Salamanca, a city so rich in cultural and artistic treasures to be considered in itself a monument. Its two cathedrals, the Old of the 12th and 13th century and the New of the 16th-17th, are famous while the Plaza Mayor is an expression of the churrigueresque style which is the Spanish version of the Baroque. The streets and the buildings glow with a particular ochre colour (because of the stone used). The warm tone of the light adds to the atmosphere of the town. But what makes Salamanca known all over the world is that it is the seat of one of the most ancient and renowned Universities. Founded in 1218 by King Alfonso IX of León, for centuries it has been a scientific and cultural landmark in Europe. In 1500, other cultural institutions of equal importance, the Escuelas Menores, were created to collaborate with the atheneum. Alfonso IX of León is remembered for having created the equivalent to the English Magna Charta in 1188. He con-

Segovia, the Alcazar.

On the left: Segovia, the Roman Aqueduct.

14   Burgos, the Cathedral.

Granada, the Alhambra. The King's Hall.

15

Salamanca, Plaza Mayor.

cluded an agreement which allowed the representatives of the aristoc-
racy and the clergy to control its judicial power. In exchange for this
power, he required an oath of faith and loyalty to the King as counsellor
and recognizing him as the supreme judge and guarantor of peace in the
realm. In 1212 at Benavente, he accepted that judges elected by the
representatives of social classes in an assembly, were competent in
judging controversy arising between sovereign power and his subjects.

One of his successors Alfonso X of León, who reigned from 1254 to 1284, was called "The Wise". He earned a place in Spanish history not so much for his political ability, but for giving to the national language and literature an unprecedented dignity. During his short reign he raised them to a level which normally would have taken centuries to be reached. A cultured man himself, he was an enlightened and generous patron of the arts. Thanks to him, Castile became an artistic and cultural reference point of European importance calling to it scholars, scientists, poets and philosophers, as was to happen later in the Italian Renaissance courts.

The University of Salamanca grew in importance and fame. In Seville was founded a course of studies with chairs in Latin and Arabic thus inviting cultural unification of Islamic and Christian tradition.

An author of scientific works comparable to those of Galileo, and of poems and hymns, Alfonso The Wise gave life also to a powerful drawing up of laws. He entrusted their compilation to a commission of court jurists and scholars of Salamanca. He personally followed the development and the content which had to be connected to the tradition of the Roman law.

All of these events are linked to one another. Each one has its stone, its portal, its sculptured sarcophagus and statues, its decorated vaults, its rising towers, its domes shining under the sun.

One looks, one reads, one remembers. And one observes that in addition to the wear and tear from time and the natural atmospheric perils, the defenseless surfaces of the monuments are exposed to pollution which is a destructive insult from our modern world to the world of the past. The evocative energy of the materials flakes away, while the stone and marble decay. We should (and we must) protect them using the best that science can provide, to prevent, to restore and to preserve.

The duende has discovered the loving care that modern scientific technology has for the art treasures of Spain. He watches with curiosity the marvellous instruments which we use today, so different from the retort of the medieval alchemist. Nevertheless, he trusts them because he feels their power and skill, and knows that this new knowledge is a distillation over the centuries from the old wisdom. He realizes that the new frontiers of modern science will not alter the boundaries of his world but on the contrary, will preserve them. Memories will continue to have a future.

18   The Riace Bronzes.

BRONZE GIANTS
COMING FROM THE SEA
COMING FROM THE MYTH

An ancient legend of Calabria tells of the arrival from the sea of the Saints Cosma and Damiano. Now every year a procession winds down to the beach from the sanctuary near Riace Superiore in the district of Reggio Calabria. Here the ritual immersion of the statues of the two saints into the waters of the Ionian sea is performed.

In mid-August of 1972 it became known that someone had discovered two huge bronze masculine statues hidden in the shoals some 300 meters in front of the coast of Riace Marina. The coincidence with the legend immediately excited the imagination and curiosity of the people in the surrounding areas. Thus, during the recovery on the 21st and 22nd of August, the beach of Riace was so crowded that it created stress and worries for the team of frog-men and technicians entrusted with the operation.

These statues were soon revealed as being masterpieces of antique art and became known everywhere as the Riace Bronzes. They have become famous not only with conoisseurs, but from the very beginning with the general public. After the discovery, the press and public opinion followed closely the events of the restoration of the two bronze giants. While the first fascinating hypothesis about their origin and identity were being put forward, people learned to recognize the different personalities of the two statues. One was proud and aggressive. The other (the so-called "one-eyed warrior") was calm and thoughtful.

The Restoration Centre of the Soprintendenza ai Beni Archeologici of Florence began its complex and difficult work in 1975 and concluded in 1980. After restoration, an exhibition of the statues in Florence which was scheduled for a period of twenty days, had to be prolonged for six months to allow over four hundred thousand people to admire the statues. Three hundred thousand more were later to have the same opportunity when a short exhibition was held at the Quirinale Palace in Rome in June and July of 1981. The two statues were finally placed in the department of subaqueous archaeology of the Museo of Reggio Calabria.

ITALY

"...the half-open mouth of the 'one-eyed warrior' from which he seems to be about to exhale a deep breath from the powerful chest."

There are generally no doubts about the enormous historical and artistical value of the Bronzes. Even after a superficial approach there is no way of escaping from the fascination that they emanate. They involve people at an emotional level much higher than a simple aesthetic pleasure would normally do.

Some of the details are astounding: the eyelashes which were miraculously preserved, the copper lips of one of the statues, the corneas of the eyes formed in ivory, the half-open mouth of the "one-eyed warrior" from which he seems to be about to exhale a deep breath

"...their peculiar features which embody pride and peacefulness, vitality and indifference."

from the powerful chest. Their imposing height of about two meters (6 1/2 feet) emphasizes their perfect anatomical and stylistical proportions, and the concept of strength and the sensation of inner beauty and harmony which are conveyed to the observer. All this is accentuated too by their peculiar features which embody pride and peacefulness, vitality and indifference. The magic of their gestures immobilized in the bronze casts seem almost to be melting into real movement and on the verge of reconquering time and space.

The Bronzes were found by pure chance in the sea in front of Riace.

21

An underwater fisherman saw in the sand near a reef, something which looked like a human arm. After digging a little, he brought to light a whole statue. He then realized that there lay another one a short distance away.

The recovery was organized and the first cleaning operations were carried out. The amazing beauty of the statues was revealed, little by little. A passionate debate to give them a history began which developed into a very wide series of studies and research.

A physical-chemical analysis was carried out in the Restoration Centre of the Soprintendenza ai Beni Archeologici of Florence. The results contributed to the decisions regarding identification of the statues, as well as the kind of restoration operations to be undertaken. First of all the investigations on the composition of bronze were carried out with an atomic, absorption spectrophotometer. These made it possible to ascertain that both the statues were made of a binary alloy of copper and tin which is typical of the Greek bronzes of the Classical period. This confirmed that the statues were made during the 5th century B.C.

Then the discovery of presence of traces of silver in the alloy of one of the statues and of the absolute lack of this material in the other, led to the conclusion that the statues had not been made in the same period nor in the same workshop. Moreover, such a hypothesis is verified by the striking difference of style of the two bronzes. After having established that the statues had been created in several pieces and then welded together, it was recognized that the right arm and the left forearm of the "one-eyed warrior" were made in a tertiary copper-tin and lead alloy and that the copper did not belong to the same batch as that of the other parts of the statue. Such differences were attributed to restoration work which probably was undertaken in the Hellenistic age. It is assumed that for unknown reasons, the statue crashed to the ground together with its pedestal and caused severe damage to the arms. Strangely, the analysis revealed a high tendency of lead also in the other statue at the point where the arm holds the shield. It appears that this statue had needed some limited restoration to the consolidation of the junction between the shield and the left hand. Such restoration could have taken place at the same time as the restoration in the other bronze. Experts were generally in agreement on the attribution of the bronzes to the 5th century. This would have been during the same period of such inestimable art treasures as the Charioteer of Delphi, the Zeus from the Artemision (now in the National Museum of Athens) and the "Chatsworth Head" (now in the British Museum). The experts debated at length on the name of the creators of the Riace Bronzes.

"...the eyelashes which were miraculously preserved..."

They proposed Miron, Phidias, Alkmenes and many other masters. However the many different opinions found agreement only on the generic connection of the statues with the Attic School.

While there are many interesting possibilities, the problem of their origin is still unsolved. It is almost a certainty that the bronzes sank to the bottom of the Ionian sea because of the wreck of the ship which carried them. Perhaps a violent storm swept the valuable load from the deck and the sails from their stays. On the same shoals of Riace further search revealed the lead rings of the sails buried in the sand. Perhaps the heavy statues were thrown overboard to lighten the ship in difficulty. No fragments of the ship were ever found during the underwater searches.

"The magic of their gestures immobilized in the bronze casts seem almost to be melting into real movement and on the verge of reconquering time and space."

In any case, the belief most widely heard is that the statues were on their way from Greece to Italy. This is a plausible theory since the Romans "imported" a great number of works of art from the Hellenic world as booty from robbery and plunder. In regard to this, there are records of the destructive raid by the armies of Cornelius Silla on the Agorà of Athens in 86 B.C. During the raid, the great and celebrated monument statues of Athens were stripped of the precious materials which adorned them. (And it seems logical that it must have been this way also with the Riace Bronzes.) Additionally, a certain number of statues, not only the two bronzes, were sent to Italy by the Roman leader. According to another opinion, the two statues might also have been part of monuments of other cities, such as Delphi or Olympia.

One set of these theories depict the bronzes as warrior heroes (and the "one-eyed warrior" even as the Athenian leader Milziades, who led his men to victory against the Persians at Marathon). Another theory concerning identification of the statues points to the fact that, except for the shields, there is no presence of any weapons in the hands of the statues. The gesture of the right arm of both the figures shows absolutely none of the energy which one presumes is needed to hold a sword or a spear. The hands have a light and relaxed appearance and the fingers are stretched as if to hold something very thin and light. Perhaps they held a sprig of olive or laurel, which was very likely made of silver. Therefore the bronzes could represent two "oplitodromes" who were the winners of the most important races run on the occasion of the great panellenic feasts by athletes who wore helmets and carried shields. They were extraordinary athletes, who had the right to be celebrated and represented with statues while alive even as the gods were. They were figures of absolute importance in the Greek society, whose competitive successes surrounded them with a heroic and even religious aura. The shield and the helmet with the sprig of silver symbol of victory, were elements which allowed all citizens regardless of status to distinguish these statues from those of the Gods, as otherwise their elegance, harmony and dignity would have made them all equals.

26   J. Constable, *Gillingham Mill, Dorset.*

JOHN CONSTABLE:
NATURE PORTRAYED

The sky...

Brightening up after a storm, vibrating in the fading light of a spring afternoon, calm and dazzling over the silence of the summer country-side: indolent, romantic, velvety, elegiac, tormented. A light that closes in on shapes, that changes, and compels our visual and emotional perception to change with it.

Nature's space, composed of the countryside, streams and rivers, rows of trees, farms, paths, a willow-tree drooping over a pond, dew and blossoms. The warm feeling experienced is made up of numerous details, but from these one discovers the deep, calm breath of infinity. By abandoning ourselves to this we perceive the harmony which created everything.

Everybody has felt such emotions when faced with a pearly dawn, or on raising his eyes to the rumbling dark clouds of an approaching storm, or participating in the serenity of a panorama of fields, woods and the countryside. Some of us may have paused to think, and then written a poem or a note in a diary or tried to capture, with paints and brushes, those details, that light, that sky. But someone accomplished this with unique mastery. His name is forever tied to landscape painting, an artistic and poetical experience, both passionate and vivacious. We are speaking of John Constable (1776 - 1837), an English painter. His paintings made the greenery of England famous and introduced a new way of contemplating the natural environment from an artistic point of view. No longer was it a mere decorative background, as an artificial setting aimed merely at emphasizing the main subject of the painting. Nature now plays the leading role where the painter participates. He observes the spectacle with an approach which is both exploratory and romantic, with an insistance that links the rigorous analysis of a situation to an exuberant poetical composition. Constable was fascinated by the capriciousness of his favourite subjects: the light conditions, the transparent air, the dampness of the ground, the mist.

J. Constable, *Study of cirrus clouds*.

28   J. Constable, *Salisbury Cathedral from the South-West*.

J. Constable, *Hampstead Heath*.

J. Constable, *A country road with trees and figures*.

29

J. Constable, *Stonehenge*.

So little is needed to surprisingly and continuously change the scene before our eyes. The power of observation of an artist who places himself in such a relationship with nature is subject to stimulation. Actually Constable's research and study activities which appear in his sketches and impressions, explain how direct relationship with such phenomena matured his artistic impulses. There is a symbolic sentence in a letter that the painter wrote to his friend John Fisher in 1824: "The task of the painter is not to compete with nature and squeeze this scene (a valley teeming with objects and almost 50 miles long) into a few inches of canvas, but to create something out of nothing. At that very moment, within him, a poet is born". That is why there is the painter who just reproduces a landscape and the painter who, while keeping faith with reality, manages to infuse the universal and fleeting spirit of beauty into his paintings. Amongst the most important discoveries of Constable are light and sky, both ever-changing elements, and at the same time, elements which confer homogeneity to a painting. One of the problems that a painter faces when he has to transfer his inspiration onto the canvas, is the choice of the technique which he should use. The solutions adopted by the English painter are astonishing for their elegance and their effectiveness. Paint, brushes and spatules become instruments to capture the transparency of the morning sun, the fleeting whiteness of the clouds, the trembling of a shadow, the freshness of the newly fallen rain, the infinite vastness of the ever-moving sky as hours and seasons slip by. Constable's artistic objectives, his new vibrant and original way of painting, his new approach towards the relationship between man and nature, constituted a fundamental lesson for all Europe. The impulse of his art had the same energy as that with which romanticism conquered the favour of public opinion, in poetry, literature, figurative arts. Perhaps it went even further, expressing feelings that can be recognized as heralding impressionism.

For such values and significance, Constable's work today is highly respected and preserved with care. Critical and philological research is supported by scientific and technical intervention to ensure the integrity of the artistic message. This is the aim of research and analysis being carried out at Birbeck College, where the Department of Chemistry, Group for Analytical Science of the London University, has its headquarters.

There, the effects of aging on colours and on their binding agents are controlled to verify the characteristics and the amount of deterioration suffered by the natural substances used in the paintings, which range from pigments to a glue made from rabbit's skin, from eggs to bee's wax. In Constable's paintings the effect of colour is fundamental to a correct understanding of the work. The artist based a great deal of his expressive capacity on the emotions that colour can stir up. Therefore scientific activities supporting restoration and preservation of works of art are directly concerned with the very existence of art. It makes a definite contribution in maintaining through the years, the meaning given by the artist to the work of art. This is the expression of the highest ideals and the possibilities of artistic achievements.

FRANS HALS:
"GENTLEMEN AND OFFICERS, TAKE UP A POSE. I'LL PAINT YOU A PORTRAIT"

Frans Hals would not listen to reason. There was no way of convincing him, not even by offering him a higher fee than the one agreed upon. He no longer wished to stay in Amsterdam. He preferred to go back to his home in Haarlem. The sittings which were necessary to complete the painting of the Civil Guards of the 11th District of the City of Amsterdam would require the people involved to travel the twenty miles of road to Haarlem. This did not bother him in the least. This happened in 1633. It is the only year that the artist, according to the records, lived for any period away from Haarlem, his life-long residence. The negotiations fell through and the client entrusted Pieter Codde (then a young painter, but who later was to build up his own reputation) with the task of finishing the painting. Nobody took the trouble to document which were the parts painted by one and which were those painted by the other, even though Frans Hals' unmistakable style permits reliable distinction. The impetuous and firm brush work of such a master as Hals – considered one of the greatest Dutch portrait painters of the 17th century – is immediately recognizable.

This is not the only anecdote regarding the history of the picture. This huge painting is almost four and a half meters by two meters (14-⅔ feet by 6-½ feet). "The meagre company" is its nickname and indeed the officers of Captain Reyner Reael do not look very flourishing.

The work is representative of the so called "group portraits" which were very fashionable from the mid-sixteenth century onwards, in a significant variation dedicated to the state police, to members of religious brotherhoods and to leaders of charitable institutions. It is also the only one of the paintings of this kind by Hals to be preserved in the Rijksmuseum of Amsterdam. The largest number of these particular paintings belong to the Frans Hals Museum in Haarlem, where the painter died in 1666. There is no documentation on his place and date of birth, which are traditionally taken to be Antwerp in 1580. His parents probably left the city as a consequence of the Spanish occupation and it is recorded that they settled in Haarlem in 1591.

This city, therefore, is the background of the artistic experience of Hals, who was a well known and respected character in the community. He was first a member (and later the director) of the Guild of St. Lucas and a member of the state police of St. George. He was introduced to the best Dutch society of his period and therefore came into contact with rich merchants, landowners, professors and scholars (including Cartesio) of whom he left us many portraits. As a matter of fact, of the 240 paintings by Hals which are known today, 195 are portraits. Considering that this kind of painting is one of the most important of the 17th century, and that Hals' contribution is considered a decisive factor to its development in both technique and evocative ideas it is self-evident as to why his works are so carefully studied and preserved. The "group portraits" in particular, masterfully emphasizing the cultural attitude towards observation of reality and research for new means of expression, which permeated all fields of 17th century art and science. They become through Hals, testimony of a contemporary society and of its values. These are the Dutch middle class. Strong through solid commercial wealth and bound together in a very united society. Identifiable by their uniforms or the style of their clothes, by their well-being, expressed by the quality but also the sobriety of small things, by their faces and the attitudes of the people. The paintings of Hals are not simply a description or a faithful reproduction of reality. He penetrates into and interpretes the character of his subjects and expresses himself with a rapid, apparently rough touch, effectively showing and immediately defining their attitudes, their features, their vitality and their psychological subtleties.

If one observes Frans Hals' paintings one realizes that – in those faces, in those expressions, in those human presences surrounded by the solidity of their world and their period – the experience of modern portraiture has already begun.

The Rijksmuseum of Amsterdam recently subjected the portrait of the Civil Guards to a complete restoration and entrusted it to the Central Research Laboratory for Objects of Arts and Science (an institute of the Ministry for Culture). The painting which had also been restored in the last century, had suffered damage caused by the application of a protective coating and the replacement of the original framework. These operations had caused actual distortion of the canvas of the painting.

Prior to the restoration of the painting it was necessary to carry out a series of X-rays and to undertake microscopic and chemical analysis.

34

"...in those human presences surrounded by the solidity of their world and their period the experience of modern portraiture has already begun."

One of the various problems to be solved was to discover the products with which the former restoration had been carried out. Another was the nature of the thinners used in the paint. When this research with the aid of sophisticated instruments of analysis had been completed, the technicians of the Laboratory of Amsterdam were able to decide on a procedure to be followed when carrying out the restoration. First came the removal of the coating of the substances which had been used in the former restoration. Then the painting underwent a special treatment to correct the distortion of the painting, by placing it in an atmosphere of 90% humidity, under a kind of plastic tent specially created for this purpose. This treatment made it possible to remedy the effects of the shrinking of the canvas, thus allowing the phases of the subsequent restoration to bring the painting back to its original beauty. The experience gained in the recovery and the conservation of this work of art has again emphasized the irreplaceable contribution made to the work of restoration by the application of modern techniques of analysis and the use of modern and sophisticated instruments.

Page 32: F. Hals, *The meagre company*, detail.

MICHELANGELO BUONARROTI:
"I AM NOT A PAINTER"

"After dusting, figure by figure, with a linen cloth, dirt was removed by rubbing carefully with slices of "penny" or even cheaper bread. And now and then, where dirt was more persistent, they dampened such bread and in this way the paintings returned to their original beauty without suffering any damage." These words from a document of the period illustrate the technique employed in one of the very first restorations carried out on the frescoes painted by Michelangelo Buonarroti in the Sistine Chapel in Rome. These frescoes are considered to be the greatest and most complex achievements of Western Art. This restoration was undertaken in the first half of the 17th century which is little more than a century after their completion. This intervention using basically "bread and water", represents only one of the many attempts made to restore the frescoes to their original beauty. They had become begrimed with dust and the smoke produced from illumination with tallow candles, and by infiltration of rain water through the arched ceilings.

Over the centuries, the cleanings with sponges and crustless bread, applications of coats of glue (probably with a view to reviving the colours), retouchings, and even repaintings (carried out in different periods using painting techniques quite different from the original ones) gravely altered the imposing frescoes. None of these however succeeded in taking away their original and genial expressive power, the sometimes brutal intensity of the representation and the emotive capacity of the scenes.

The stories described in Michelangelo's paintings create a prodigious sensation. These are painted narratives, produced by a man's conception of religion, of history, of architecture, of artistic messages, which Buonarroti perfected and experienced in a unique manner. Michelangelo as a man and as an artist possessed only one conscience, only one philosophy and only one objective. That being torment and anxiety, desperate and heroic awareness that the fullfillment of life and

ITALY

Michelangelo, Sistine Chapel, *God creating Adam*, detail.

art is to be sought in death. Not humbly sought with resignation, but with a deeply vital impulse which is both heroic and tragic.

Commissioned by Pope Sixtus IV, the Sistine Chapel in the Vatican City is a milestone in art for all time. Also a milestone is the history of its restoration. The Restoration Department of the Vatican Museums has been working for many years on an enterprise which is at the same time artistic, scientific and cultural. Each one of these aspects is of fundamental importance. The work on analytical examination of the frescoes of the Sistine Chapel was long and indispensable in every one of its meticulous details. Infrared spectrometry, liquid chromatography and atomic absorption spectrophotometry were used to identify extraneous substances, the pigments used by Michelangelo, the paints applied above them by the restorers in the course of centuries and the elements which had been responsible for the deterioration. Then decisions had to be taken on the techniques that were to be used to clean the frescoed walls and vaulted ceilings and the manner of the subsequent steps of the restoration work. The time needed to complete the entire work was estimated to be about twelve years.

In 1987, the first series of the restoration had been concluded and the Sistine Chapel was opened to the public again. The sensation created by the comparison between the parts which had undergone the complex restoration and those which still had to be cleaned, was astounding. It was somewhat like looking at a colour photograph in the

Page 36: Michelangelo, *Last Judgement*.
On the right: Michelangelo, Sistine Chapel, the vault.

restored area and at a black and white one in the unrestored portion (upon which art historians had always founded their judgement of Michelangelo's work). It now appears that the fundamental elements regarding the artistic analysis of the Sistine Chapel have been, and will further be, completely reversed by results achieved by the Restoration Department of the Vatican Museums.

The cleaning was carried out with special thinners and revealed how some ancient restoration had completely replaced the original colours in some areas of the frescoes. The revival of the chromatic values to the quality originally painted by Michelangelo which were able to incite a particular kind of visual and emotive impact to the viewer, gives a new explanation of the logic of the artist. Until now he was esteemed principally for his skill in modelling forms and volumes rather than for his newly found personality in the use of colour. Some interventions have been identified which even altered the original drawing. It also became possible to be specific about Michelangelo's technique of painting thus confirming with precise situations the connecting links in Michelangelo's life. For example the restored painting show that Michelangelo was a perfect master of the fresco technique and followed the teachings and the rules of Ghirlandaio's Florentine workshop, where he had worked for a long time in his youth during a period of "artistic apprenticeship".

Precise evidence shows that the work was accomplished while Michelangelo was going through many different psychological moments. He worked methodically, reflecting on his paintings and often correcting his first designs. He also used to paint while driven by his vivid inspiration, improvising, impelled by an incredible creative impulse which led him to do without the preparatory steps of the frescoes. Certainly there were also periods when improvisation was simply due to haste when he was behind in his schedule.

Michelangelo began to work in the Sistine Chapel in May 1508 and 540 square meters (5700 square feet) were to be painted. Michelangelo was engaged for the work by Pope Julius II, who had to persuade the reluctant artist by insisting that it be done. In a famous sonnet, Michelangelo weighed up the extreme difficulty of working on scaffolding and protested that anyhow "he was not a painter". Moreover he had already taken on the task of building the complex monumental tomb of Julius II. Nevertheless he set about the work and by 1512 the frescoes of the ceiling were completed. The genius of Michelangelo, notwithstanding his reluctance to try out his hand at using colours and brushes, was handed down to history also in the field of painting.

40   In 1535 another pope, Paul III, entrusted Michelangelo with the

Michelangelo, Sistine Chapel, details of figures during and after restoration.

completion of the Chapel by painting the wall behind the main altar. In five years, from 1536 to 1541, Michelangelo painted "a fresco" of about 350 square meters (3700 square feet). He created his "Last Judgement" which so dramatically expresses the artist's arduous approach towards life and religion. It was done in a period in his life of profound crisis when he was faced with the historical events and the political and ideological changes brought about by the tumultuous society of the 16th century. There is a curious episode amongst the anecdotes which go side-by-side with art history. It was later deemed for reasons of decency, that the hundreds of nude figures of the imposing painting had to be moralized. Another painter, Daniele da Volterra, was entrusted with the task of "clothing" the nudes, by placing here and there, suitable coverings. The artist who also produced a large number of valuable paintings, paid dearly for this assignment. For, when seen by posterity, he earned himself the ironical nickname of "Il Braghettone" (the pants maker or the breeches maker).

El Fayum,
funeral portrait of Aline,
known as
42 "The Girl of Berlin".

THE GAZE OF A WOMAN:
THE MYSTERY OF LIFE BEYOND ITS SPAN

Her gaze is vast and deep, lost in thought. It is disconcerting but sweet; intense, but melancholy; dreamy yet pure under the well marked curve of the eyebrows. Deep down in those dark eyes, in the depths of who knows what secret memories, a light gleams. It seems still alive, even though it comes from far away in terms of space and time.

Her oval and diminutive face framed by black curls, is not what could really be called beautiful. But it expresses such mysterious and persuasive feminine charm that it became one of the most fascinating faces of all times. It is a romantic face of a woman who lived eighteen centuries ago in the Roman provinces of Egypt. Her name was Aline, but today everybody knows her as "The Girl of Berlin", because her portrait which is a unique and extraordinary testimony of her existence, is preserved in the Staatliche Museen of Berlin.

This famous painting is one of many, of both men and women, called the "Portraits of El-Fayum". El-Fayum is an oasis in the Libyan desert where some of the portraits were unearthed. Usually painted in wax on wooden panels, they were also found in other areas, but were always inside tombs buried under the dry sand of the desert. This had miraculously preserved these precious exhibits which date back to a period between the first and the fourth century A.D.

What these portraits have in common is that they are probably the only "easel paintings" which have reached us from ancient times. All the paintings are linked to one another by the Egyptian custom of placing a portrait of the deceased on the mummified corpse. Very often however, the portraits were not painted at the time of death but depict the years of youth, thus preserving for the future the memory of the beauty and sentimental vigour of the best days of their lives.

Even though the existance of the El-Fayum portraits can be connected with funeral traditions of Pharaonic origin, the artistic features show clear evidence of the Hellenistic and Roman models. Study of the details give us information about the introduction of Roman habits and

GERMANY

customs into the Egyptian society. Moreover, it also tells us of the ethnical and social complexities of a territory where Roman colonials, African people, Greek immigrants and Semitic races lived together.

Scholars have widely examined the historical and cultural background of the paintings. The artistic knowledge which these portraits convey to us with their different styles, constitutes a salient moment in the history and evolution of ancient painting. They are considered to be the starting point of that artistic journey which was to express images of Christian art and of Byzantine mosaics.

From a technical point of view, the El-Fayum portraits are considered to be the oldest paintings on wood to reach us from ancient times. Scattered throughout the best museums of the world, they have also been studied using scientific equipment and methods. Using infrared spectrometry, the role and features of the wax were checked. In such a technique, known as "encaustic paintings", wax functions as a colour fixative to keep the paint in place. In practice the wax was melted, mixed with the colours and then applied while hot. This is the oldest technique and also one of the most complicated due to the obvious necessity of working with hot melted wax and spreading it with quick strokes of the brush. Later on natural wax was subject to particular treatment by adding an alkaline solution using soda or other salts drawn from deposits from the area as a base. This produced a very pliable paste known as "Punic wax" that was workable using metal or wooden spatulas at a temperature lower than its melting point. Despite the particulars that can be determined using the sophisticated technical features of the equipment, the magic fascination of the "Girl of Berlin" remains unchanged. This painting best expresses the charm of all of the paintings of the series of the "Portraits of El-Fayum" which is the extraordinary expression of their proud and dreamy eyes. Without venturing into complex learned comparisons, one instantly notices the resemblance between the portrait of the thoughtful Aline and some works of the French Impressionists. For instance, the soft brushwork of certain sensual paintings of Renoir which portray the same kind of young women who are fragile but strong, graceful but intense. These were the leading ladies of the middle class romantic experiences of the 19th century in society, literature and art.

There is also another more subtle emotion which marks the approach to the "Girl of Berlin" and the other portraits. It goes beyond all considerations of historical, artistic and scientific values and wipes out the depth of centuries and centuries.

While only a portrait composed of wood, wax and pigmentation, within its beauty it also conceals a rational idea. There is a vital flash in

El Fayum, funeral portrait of a woman.

El Fayum, funeral portrait of a woman.

El Fayum, funeral portrait of the archon of
Thebes (second century A.D.).

46

the features of the painted face and whoever manages to perceive it is found grappling with an idea that the portrait is a symbol. Concealed in the deep eyes of Aline lies the secret of another dimension similar to our own where thousands of years are but the blinking of an eye and limitless knowledge and serenity are the answer to the tormented dilemma of Life and Death. Thanks to fortunate climatic conditions and mere chance, hundreds of faces still alive with enigmatic gazes, have been preserved. They are a small group of characters with intense and immense eyes who came out of the secret of their sarcophagi and have been scattered throughout the world. They represent a peaceful invasion of unknown people, so similar to us in features, yet so different. They can transmit a feeling of life and mystery to those who stop to peer at the waxen pupils of their eyes.

Wreath of golden oak leaves coming from the Macedonian royal tombs discovered at
Vergina in 1977.

MACEDONIA:
BETWEEN HISTORY AND MYTH,
BETWEEN THE HUMAN AND THE DIVINE

The descendants of Makedon, the ancestor of a divine race, formed a community which wanted as its own land, not a wide and fertile plain, but a mountainous and difficult territory in the north of Greece: Macedonia.

In such places destiny had ordained that the energy and the responsibility to modify the history of the world should mature slowly. The blood of those people, blended with the mysterious substance which runs in the veins of the gods, waited until the year 356 B.C. before giving birth to a ruler, Alexander the Great. He was so great that he left in his mere thirty-three years of life, a distinct mark on the ill-defined and teeming mosaic of the life of humanity as few other men before and after him were able to do.

The mere breath of a story dedicated to this great figure and to the Macedonians, would call for a strict rhythm of historical reconstruction. But for over two thousand years, it has been a narrative which takes hold of you with the ease of short exciting gusts of the rarified air of legend and myth.

History and myth are two faces of man in his journey through the ages. At times it is impossible to distinguish one from the other. Fascinating features appear and it seems natural not to resist and to let them conquer us. Then everything is credible, even that the ancient events of the Macedonian people were entwined with those of the Gods, that certain lives had been spent on the boundaries between reality and fantasy, and that certain historical events inevitably followed the omens of the oracles.

All this belongs to a world and to a people that contemporaries considered almost uncivilized and forever intimately tied to a barbaric past. Sophisticated Athens, civilized Sparta and cultured Thebes looked with suspicion on certain violent customs, certain over-exuberant vitality and certain exaggerated fierce traditions.

A Macedonian king could, like the humblest of his soldiers, fight and

GREECE

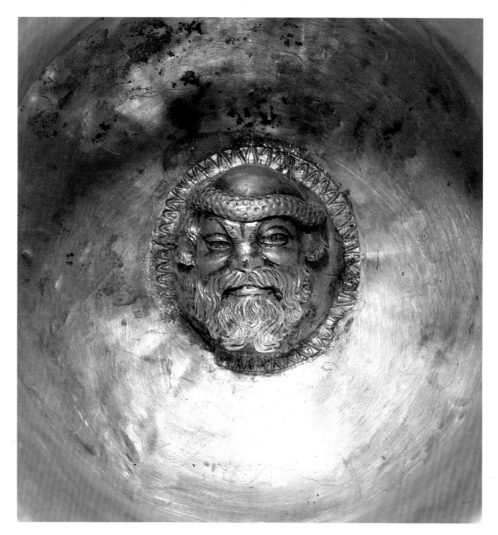

Head of drunken Silenus. The medallion decorates the bottom of a silver goblet coming from Philip's Tomb.

hunt completely naked. He could get drunk without restraint and amuse himself rowdily. Dark, strong and endowed with the ancestral energy of the earliest nomadic tribes, the Macedonians let their hair and beards grow, fought in battle with intelligence and ferocity, and, their fame as heroes would forever be associated with a certain amount of roughness and brutality. This inspite of their progressive adjustment to a social and cultural model of the Greek order and the creation of disciplined cities, roads and temples.

Alexander, the semi-god conquerer, the pupil of Aristotle. Alexan-

Philip's Tomb. Iron armour with golden ornamental patterns.

der, who slept with the Iliad, but also had a dagger under his pillow. Alexander the ceaseless leader, who respectfully stepped aside when the famous Diogenes told him to move, because his body obscured the sun and cast a shade which the philosopher did not like. Alexander the master of half the world who was capable both of merciless trials of strength as he was of noble and gentle actions. Alexander was born under the sign of Leo, while Aries was rising above the horizon. These are both signs of fire, with the imprint of the Sun, the star which symbolizes both the god creating Ammon, and Mars the god of war.   51

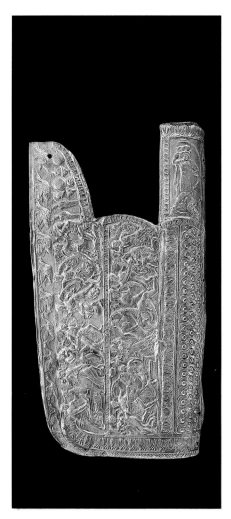

Philip's Tomb. Golden ornamental covering for the container of a bow and arrows. Big silver vase with Silenus's head. Two of them were found in Philip's Tomb.

These were unmistakable omens of what was about to happen. On the same day of Alexander's birth occurred the terrible fire of the Temple of Diana at Ephesus. This burning spirit which was to guide Alexander, and which deigned the Hellenistic world to expand and blend harmoniously with other civilizations, produced a new entity. One culturally capable of unifying different experiences and one whose splendour still shines amongst us today.

Around this great figure revolve others who complete the story.

A thousand stories interlace and vivaciously draw almost a living

Philip's tomb. Golden casket. The sixteen pointed star was the emblem of the Macedonian royal dynasty.

picture. Alexander's father, Philip, was the originator of the first Macedonian expansion and succeeded in creating the first confederation of Greek states. He was a warrior covered with scars, a phenomenal drinker and a philander, a fiery leader and a machiavellian strategist. The Greek philosopher Demostenes launched his verbal attacks against him which became famous as "Philippics". Alexander's mother Olympia was a priestess of orgiastic cults. She was wrapped up in the sinister veils of mysterious and violent rituals and was convinced that she had conceived Alexander from a god who incarnated himself as a serpent. She bestowed special attention on the serpent, rather than her husband and dreamed that she gave birth to a serpent of fire before the birth of Alexander.

Another female figure who influenced Alexander's lineage was his grandmother, Euridice. A brutal queen who committed hideous crimes she exterminated her family and was finally killed by the only survivor, her son Philip, the future king of Macedonia. Also, inseparable from Alexander, is his friend Ephesion, a very handsome young man who was his companion in life and in war and a beloved new Patroclus. There are many more names, all immortal. Names of kings, of generals, of priests, of beautiful women, of philosophers, of artists, of historians. But in this story appear also humble soldiers, defeated enemies, cruelly punished traitors. All of them bring back the mythical images of famous cities, of temples, of unexplored lands, of unknown people and languages.

Historical sources, myths, legends drawn from famous tragic or poetic texts, testimonies elaborated in a literary form, are words of enormous descriptive power. But they always remain just words. On the contrary, tangible indeed are the archaeological exhibits with their astonishing beauty, which came mostly from monumental tombs but also from excavations which brought to light ancient buildings or urban centers. A great number of these objects are preserved in the Museum of Thessalonike. Here the charm and fascination of such a distant past has been fully evaluated through the use of extremely modern equipment and avant-garde technology including the atomic absorption spectrophotometer which is essential to deepen research into the materials to establish the date when they were made and to provide direction on the best technique of restoration and conservation.

The treasures of the Museum of Thessalonike are a tangible testimony of a people and a revelation of its customs and traditions. Famous exhibitions of some of those treasures have been held in New York, Chicago, Boston, San Francisco, Washington and also in Bologna, Italy.

Objects which belong to everyday life, exceptional funeral regalia and finely made ornaments convey in human terms the mythical history of the people. They testify indeed of a civilization with precise aestethical standards and artistic tendencies, supported by great technical skills. It is surprising to realize how this population, whose fame is linked to concepts of strength, exuberance and aggressive war, could work with embossed, chiselled or engraved metal, creating really true works of art. That they could use refined and expressive techniques in painting, could venture into the art of mosaics and could dedicate themselves to creating incredibly elegant and stylish gold jewellery.

Even the Macedonian tombs represent particular phenomena of special interest. They were subterranean buildings with vaulted ceilings and were made of single or double rooms and covered with a conical mound. Although often plundered, some of these tombs have remained intact. This allowed archaeologists to make some exciting discoveries such as the famous royal tombs of Vergina, the ancient Aigai, the capital city of the Macedonians and the burial place of Kings.

The last resting place of Philip II, Alexander's father, who died in 336 B.C., contained the royal diadem, the golden crown, weapons, silver and bronze plate and two golden urns which contained the ashes of the king and those of a mysterious woman. The Museum of Thessalonike, among the numerous exhibits, has custody of the results of many other findings. Included are clay amphorae, parts of armours, decorated goblets, utensils made of precious metals, jewels and the famous wreaths of golden leaves. All of these creations are of such miraculous refinement that they arouse fantastic imagination, as if they had been created by hands possessing divine skill, and destined to wreathe the brows of those personalities endowed with divine knowledge. Once more Myth murmurs irresistible suggestions to the writings of history.

Golden decoration in the shape of the magic knot of Hercules.

56   Bronze group from Cartoceto. The statue of Livia.

A MYSTERY STORY FROM IMPERIAL ROME: THE BRONZE GROUP FROM CARTOCETO

Fragments of gilded bronze are often fragments of history.

Research and suppositions, decades of study and restoration work have brought back life to a group of ancient statues. They have disclosed not only a form of art, but also the nature of life so very far away. The statues evoke memories of a period murky with intrigues along with memories of those people who some artist represented in bronze in ancient times.

This requires uncertain journeys amongst hardly intelligible echoes of events that happened almost two thousand years ago. Patient investigation which combined the intuition and the rigour of the human mind with the analytical precision of extremely modern instruments also played their part in the enthusiasm we experience when facing the mystery of the "Bronzes from Cartoceto".

This precious one-of-a-kind bronze group is composed of four human figures and two horses. It is considered to be among the best examples of Roman equestrian sculptures. The historical and artistical interpretation takes us back to Imperial Rome in the first years after the birth of Christ. This journey back through the centuries began by mere chance. On the 26th of June 1946, at Cartoceto, a locality near Pergola in the province of Perugia, two farm labourers while digging a ditch near their home saw a leg of a bronze horse sticking out of the earth. In the ensuing days while digging in a wider area, other parts of the horse and the head of a female figure were found. Almost one ton of fragmentary pieces had been recovered. The incrustations obscured the rich gilding of the surfaces and the pieces were so small that it was difficult to gather a general idea of the work of art as a whole. Nevertheless there was no doubt that what had been unearthed at Cartoceto was an exceptional archaeological discovery.

Documentation on the restoration, the physical-chemical research, the conservation work, the reconstruction, the studies and the interpretations were developing little by little. These items regarding the

ITALY

characters represented in the group and about the entangled history of the monument itself, make up a bulky dossier.

The group portrayed includes Livia – first the wife of Claudius Nero and then of Augustus, and also the mother of Tiberius. Also included in the group are two young men, Drusus Caesar and Nero Caesar. After Tiberius, they were both candidates for succession to the imperial throne. Due to political affairs and obscure court intrigues, which at that time were often the same thing, both of them came to a sticky end. Nero Caesar and his mother Agrippina the Elder (represented by the second female figure in the bronze group) were exiled while Drusus disappeared into the dungeons of the palace on the Palatine. The three were condemned for the worst of crimes. They were judged to be enemies of the State. This defamatory mark could explain the destruction of the statues, which surely came about in ancient times. In fact in Rome there existed a procedure to physically obliterate traces of the existence of those who had been condemned. This included even bronze statues. "Abolitio memoriae" was the technical term for this procedure which, with some variant, emphasized the punishment. The statue of Tiberius, which very probably dominated the group, was saved. The statues of the two princes and of their mother were subject to the violence of clubs and picks.

The same thing happened to the statue of Livia because of Sejanus's hatred towards her. Livia was one of the most famous women in Roman history because of the influence she had in the state's affairs as well as for her character and her moral qualities. Sejanus was the "eminence gris" of the empire and had succeeded in eliminating the two unwelcome successors to Tiberius. Livia had the good fortune to die in her own bed, a rare event in those days. Thus, deprived of the possibility of doing her physical harm, Sejanus gave vent to his grudge by involving the statue of this woman in the "abolitio memoriae". It must be pointed out that the bronze group from Cartoceto is a copy of the original which is believed to have found its place in Rome and which was reproduced in large numbers.

A very short time elapsed between the glorification and the condemnation of the monument. It was constructed between 23 and 29 A.D. and its destruction took place in 30 A.D. The executors of the "abolitio memoriae" ruthlessly attacked the faces of the crown princes and that of Agrippina the Elder, but were less brutal with the two horses and the statue of Livia. The horses are considered today as being the most remarkable examples of Roman equestrian sculpture. The whole group was buried despite the fact that Romans prized bronze highly and treasured such material. They simply changed the heads of the statues

"Livia was one of the most famous women in Roman history because of the influence she had in the state's affairs as well as for her character and her moral qualities."

of the personalities who had fallen into disgrace or who were no longer "public figures". This burial aimed at highlighting the removal of the statues and also brought additional disgrace to the group. Why the group ended up in a hole in the ground near Cartoceto – then an almost forgotten barren land which is far from lines of communication – is one of the many mysteries of this story. If the theory is true that the group had been placed in an important centre of the Marche region, for example Fano, it could possibly be that the choice of the burial place was due to an excess of zeal to send the disfigured statues to the boundaries of the municipality.

Many details, which have emerged from the study of the bronzes and verified on the basis of information from historical sources, lend themselves to other interpretations, all of which are impressive and plausible.

The head of one of the two horses of the bronze group from Cartoceto, considered among the most remarkable examples of Roman equestrian sculpture.

Leaving to the experts the task of continuing the research, there is one piece of information worth mentioning, reported by Svetonio, which assigns to these characters a less defamatory historical remembrance. Nero Caesar and Drusus Caesar had a brother, evidently more fortunate than they, who became Emperor with the gloomy but celebrated name of Caligula.

Caligula rehabilitated the good name of his brothers and of his mother, recovered their ashes and meritoriously placed them in the Mausoleum of

Bronze group from Cartoceto. Nero Caesar.

Augustus. He even ordered the sculpture of some statues dedicated to them and also probably reproduced their images on coins of a new series.

The business of the restoration of the "Bronzes from Cartoceto" is complex and eventful. It took decades of activity involving the transfer of the fragments of the group from the Museo Nazionale in Ancona (to which it belongs) to the Soprintendenza ai Beni Archeologici of Tuscany. Here it seemed as though the fate of destiny had locked away for posterity the sentence of the ancient Roman Tribunal. The cases con-

61

taining the fragments of the bronzes, after being stored for a while in Florence, were submerged in mud during the flood of 1966. Thus the effects of the "abolitio memoriae" (and in its particular form of a new burial, called "repositio") were renewed and continued until 1974, when the forgotten bronze fragments were recovered and consigned to the Restoration Centre of the Soprintendenza of Florence. Among the chemical-physical studies which were carried out, of importance were the ones directed towards determining the composition of the alloy used to cast the bronzes. One of the first elements to emerge was the high percentage of lead in the alloy, characteristic of the cast produced in the Roman workshops of the period during which it is considered that the statues were made. This confirmed the accuracy of the historical dating.

The analytical results established that the bronze used for the casts was from a single source and that the small traces of different elements were due to different melting processes in the crucibles.

Furthermore, for reasons strictly connected with the choice of the restoration techniques to be adopted, it was essential to ascertain whether the gilding had been carried out using an amalgamation with mercury, or made to adhere to the statues with glue or simply applied under pressure. The conclusion of the analytical studies was that the gilding had been carried out using pressure, and that between the gold leaf and the bronze, oxidation or electrochemical corrosion had created a layer of carbonates similar to those which covered the gilding itself. Consequently, the cleaning had to be carried out exclusively by hand, using lancets and a microscope. About one thousand days of work were needed on the surface of about six square meters (63 square feet) at the pace of forty to ninety square centimeters a day. In total, technicians and specialists of the Restoration Centre, chemists, physicists, photographers, designers and laboratory assistants dedicated to the restoration of the bronze group no less than forty-five thousand hours of work.

On the left: copy of the equestrian statue of Nero Caesar.

ttnieteintent hst laiettelh   des romains· Et anoit autant de dilhance
de iemis· ¶ Apies leoit   du·Roy au Roy des romains come du
lempuiim· ¶ Apies leoit   Roy a lempueur· Et anoient lempuem
le Roy ainlctoine ou miheu   le Roy et le Roy des romains chakun se
du trour de la sale· ¶ Apies   puement vn kiel de diap dor tolde de ielu
le Roy de tianke leoit le toy   au aus armes de tianke· et par dellus ieulx

IN NO WAY A GLASS SLIPPER

Listen to this story... A log burns tirelessly in the enormous fireplace. The soft light of the flames flickers towards the centre of the great hall and entwines with that of the wall torches, making the shadows tremble continuously on the stone walls, in the deep arches of the windows and among the figures of a large tableau in the far background.

Round the massive oak table laden with trays still full of food, are seated ladies and knights. They are beautiful in the lustruous candle-light of the many elements of the chandelier and elegantly clad in precious clothes. Gorged with excellently cooked food fragrant with juniper and fine herbs and having set aside the pleasures of the banquet and of the conversation, they relax to listen to a dark-haired young man who is reciting his verses while standing in front of the table. He is not part of the group. This can readily be seen from his humble yet fanciful clothes, and from his accent which is typical of the southern counties. He is one of those wandering minstrels, without home and without an aim. Perhaps one day they will become famous, but certainly for many more days to come they will be enriched only by their verses and their dreams of glory.

But what is sure is that he is a poet. The emotions stirred up by his intense acting are heightened by a boy crouched on a stool who plays soft and charming tunes on a flute. The guests listen to his recollections of a lost love and the sorrow for being unable to find it again. He tells of efforts to defeat the dragon, to conquer a gloomy fortress, to cross an ice floe, to penetrate into the mystery of a sunless forest, to venture into the labyrinths of caves which lead to the burning heart of the highest mountain in the world. All this to no avail since the beloved girl had been abducted through adverse destiny which will never allow her, and he who yearns for her, even the shortest moment of happiness.

A young damsel among the guests watches the poet with intensity. She wears a dark green dress which stiffly rises from her shoulders along her long neck, which makes her appear slender and fragile.

FRANCE

Around the perfect oval of her face, an abundance of auburn hair is stubbornly kept in style by velvet ribbons of the same colour as that of the dress. Her eyes are also green and flash with golden light both inviting and irresistible. It is not the story of the knight in love, but other mysterious thoughts which make her gaze so warm and her smile so gentle and sweet. The poet has noticed it and falters on a rhyme. The charm of those sparkling green eyes encircles him like a spell. He no longer simply recites, but passionately addresses himself to the young lady in front of him. The verses of his poem seem to have for the first time a true meaning as they appeal for love, as they ask for some sign, and as they implore at least a hope.

The damsel has understood and with a flutter of her eyelashes asks him to be patient, to wait. However, the knight sitting by her side, is also aware that something odd is going on and evidently does not approve of her being a party of a dialogue with the poet. His irritation has already wrinkled his brow. He has squared his shoulders and he squirms on his bench while his left foot begins to tap out an impatient and menacing rhythm on the floor.

The poet has understood the message. The top of the oak table equally divides, symbolically, his field of vision. In the upper half a charming face that expresses a wonderful promise. In the lower half, the nervous foot in an elegant boot of soft leather of the kind that only rich gentlemen can afford with a long pointed toe and a broad turn over at the calf.

These are points that a minstrel must take into serious consideration unless he wants to be thrown out of the castle without reward and without supper. Or worse, with a kick in the seat of his pants. And notwithstanding the quality of the shoe that does it, it hurts both your body and your pride to be kicked out. Wisdom often has little to do with happiness so the poet makes a sign to his young musician who skillfully passes over to a new vivacious song without sighs of love. The story also changes along with the music. No more verses about courteous love. The poet lustily strikes up with a recital about the heroic deeds of pure, dauntless knights in exotic countries, and oddly enough, without female characters. A glance to the foot under the table. It is now calm in its comfortable shoe. A last thrill from the green eyes shining with golden light. Then the poet forces himself to look at the other guests and to lose himself in the emptiness of the room behind them, towards the flames in the fireplace. Tomorrow another castle, he thinks, to quell his disappointment. "And if, passing near the mill on the stream, I again meet that blonde girl with the white bonnet and freckled nose, I'll learn how to forget those green cat's eyes of the

66

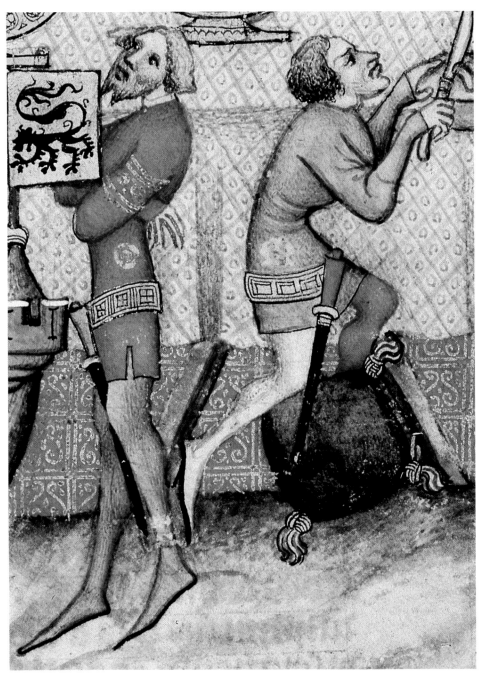

"…an elegant boot of soft leather of the kind that only rich gentlemen can afford with
a long pointed toe and a broad turn over at the calf."
Page 64: French miniature of XIV century.

The "Pologne" of Saint-Denis.

princess. A curse on me and on the feet of all jealous knights. If I was one of those who can walk in such beautiful boots I wouldn't worry about my damsel casting a glance at a minstrel. I'd wait for her to count the holes in the soles of his shoes and the patches on his pants... Ladies who don't care about these things only exist in my tales".

All this could have taken place in a French castle at the end of the 14th century. In any case a shoe like the one of the jealous knight of our story is preserved today in the Unité d'Archéologie of Saint-Denis, near Paris. It was recovered after being buried for such a long time, during an excavation undertaken just near Saint-Denis and it is a very rare object. Leather is a material which deteriorates very easily. Therefore it is not often that such antique exhibits are found. Its preservation over the years has to be because of the nature of the soil in which it was found. The shoe was soaked with water and appeared to be intact or almost so, as were other leather objects – belts, knife sheaths and gloves recovered in the same place.

The shoe belongs to the end of the 14th century. Leather craftmanship, practised in France from Carolingian period, had reached a remarkable degree of refinement.

This is also demonstrated by some paintings of the same period. In a painting which shows a banquet offered by the French King Charles V to the Emperor Charles IV, footwear of the same kind as that found at Saint-Denis are visible. Originally they were not produced according to French taste. The fashion for these boots favoured by nobleman, came from Poland, hence their name "Pologne". Their shape, with a long, pointed toe, was not their only characteristic. At ankle level it was customary to apply a crenellated decoration, while the lacing was only on one side of the boot.

Once the "Pologne" from Saint-Denis had been recovered, the method of preserving it had to be studied. The leather, so very soaked with water, risked irreparable damage from the moment it started to dry out. Making the most out of the special techniques used by the Centre de Recherches sur la Conservation des Documents Graphiques in Paris (where the ancient leather bindings of the precious volumes and the parchment of important documents are "treated"), the shoe was freeze-dried thus making the water evaporate without causing hardening of the leather. Later the various parts were sewn together using the technique of medieval shoemakers, with stitches which faithfully followed the original holes. So today's "Pologne" has returned and is identical to that worn by the fourteenth-century knight of our story.

MARY ROSE:
A SWEET NAME FOR THE FLAGSHIP
OF THE TUDORS

Beautiful and big, its flanks bristling with guns, its thirty-two meters keel and the sweet name of a woman: Mary Rose. The flagship of Henry VIII, whose name is still remembered today for his considerable number of wives, mistresses and daughters, could only have been christened a female.

The Mary Rose was the flagship of the Royal Navy and the symbolic jewel of Tudor sea power. The powerful sailing vessel was, however, doomed to an unglorious end. In 1545 she set sail from Portsmouth to face the French fleet. (These were years of bitter tension. In Europe, wars for religious and political reasons were breaking out everywhere. And across the ocean the New World was experiencing harsh and merciless methods of conquest.) After reaching the open sea and even before she had opened fire, the ship listed to one side and sank rapidly in the icy waters of the English Channel. It is said that Henry VIII, who had taken up a position with his soldiers on the coast at Southsea Common, heard the shouts of the crew and the desperate cries for help of the seven hundred people who were struggling against death among the waves.

There is a strange coincidence between the life span of the Mary Rose and the years of the reign of Henry VIII. He ascended to the throne in 1509 and in the same year the flagship was built. Henry died in 1547, only two years after the ship had sunk.

The sailing vessel remained submerged until 1982. An extraordinary and closely followed recovery operation, patronized by Prince Charles and considered as a national event all over Great Britain, brought the hull to the surface. Four hundred and thirty-seven years are a really long time, even for such a strong and solid framework as that of the Mary Rose which was built of solid oak. Sea water erosion had severely damaged almost half the vessel while the part which had remained covered by the mud and the sediment of the sea bed was preserved in better condition.

In addition to the complex questions relating to the raising technique, two different problems had to be faced, with all the worries that wrong decisions could lead to irreparable consequences. First problem was what should be done immediately after the hull had been permanently located in a dry place to avoid destructive processes even more serious than those which had happened beneath the sea. The second problem was how to tackle the long term work of restoration and definite preservation.

"...a period of great ventures in navigation, of ever-bolder journeys across the oceans, of geographical discoveries and colonial expansion, of military glory and celebrated adventures of piracy."
Page 70 and here above: English vessel of XVI century.

These two problems were further complicated by the anticipation of a different reaction of the two parts of the ship to the change of environment since one had been protected by the mud and the other exposed to the sea water. The first action initiated by a team of technicians was to recreate around the Mary Rose a situation similar to the one in which she had been located for centuries. In a specially equipped dry dock at Portsmouth the ship is kept at a constant level of humidity of

The port of Dover in an English drawing of XVI century.

95% and at a temperature of 5° centigrade (41°F). In practice, chilled water is being finely sprayed around the hull 20 hours a day. The Mary Rose will remain in this condition until the completion of the research on the techniques to be employed to remove the ship from this "water cloud", dry it and proceed to its restoration.

In particular, a treatment using polyethylene glycol is being perfected in order to preserve the wood of the ship. This substance penetrates into the wood thus eliminating break up resulting from the drying out. When the task of consolidation of the structure is concluded after several years' work, the humidity will be gradually reduced inside the dry dock where the Mary Rose is kept. Then the real phases of the restoration work will begin.

Such a long wait however will not diminish interest in the famous Tudor flagship. This valuable recovery has shed light on the kind of life that ship crews led more than four hundred years ago. This is indeed a relevant aspect in Great Britain's social and cultural history because of its relationship with the sea and with the navy. To know that world is all the more important when we consider that it was a period of great ventures in navigation, of ever-bolder journeys across the oceans, of geographical discoveries and colonial expansion, of military glory and celebrated adventures of piracy. All this is forever tied to the names of great and small ships, to the lives of mostly unknown men, who on board those ships spent a hard and often violent life. But also at times a patient, courageous and sometimes heroic existence.

Other than being kept constantly to the forefront by the massmedia and the scholars, the Mary Rose is well known in England for other reasons. For instance it is the subject of several special courses undertaken by high-school students to gain a better understanding of their mother tongue.

Furthermore, at Portsmouth a museum has been opened which recreates situations typical of life on board by exhibiting some of the objects which were found in the Mary Rose.

An inestimable heritage, the 13,702 exhibits range from heavy cannon carriages to a pocket sun-dial carved from wood, from leather work articles to musical instruments, from bows and arrows to sailors' and carpenters' tools, from pastime games to various kinds of clothes. Undoubtedly aboard the Mary Rose was a strange character (half surgeon and half barber) who with little knowledge and much experience along with a good deal of improvisation, took care of the crew's health. In his small trunk was found a jar of ointment, which even after so many centuries still bears the fingerprint of the person who had used it. It may have been used to heal a wound on the shoulder of a young, inexperienced ship-boy, who during one of his first dizzy climbs up the main mast and amongst the sails, had slipped and fallen and then was miraculously caught in the rigging. A freckled-faced boy whom the boatswain had to disentangle from the ropes which had harshly grazed his bare skin. The same ropes thanks to which his deadly flight had turned into a short fall. And the gruff old sea-dog, faced with the humiliating embarassment of the terrorized boy (brought trembling and aching to the deck amidst the sneers of the sailors) sent the greenhorn to the surgeon-barber to have his back healed with a little

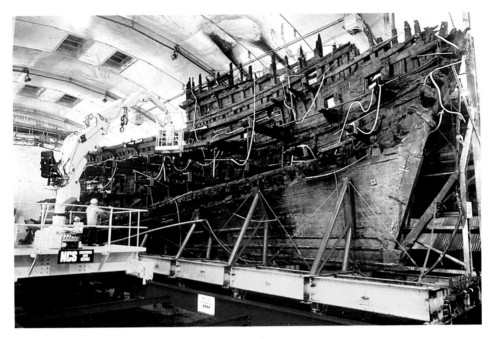

The Mary Rose in the dry-dock at Portsmouth.

ointment. He told him also to be sure that he was given ointment, because the night before the eccentric surgeon had gotten blind drunk in one of the port's tavern. With his hangover, there was the risk that he might extract one of the poor boy's teeth or give him one of his deadly purgatives instead of spreading on his shoulders the stinking but beneficial ointment. Who can tell looking at the fingerprints left on the jar, that this is not a true story?

76   P. Picasso, *Seated Woman* (1938).

PABLO PICASSO:
A REVOLUTIONARY ENCOUNTER
BETWEEN MAN AND ART

The problem of conservation and restoration of works of art, and the consequential search for appropriate technological application, does not concern only the art treasures which have been accumulated by man in the course of past centuries. The attention of researchers, scholars and technicians is focused also on the problem of preserving the contemporary art and artistic monuments of great modern artists.

The objective is always to preserve the material in which the artistic expression is embodied, thus ensuring its immunity from the attack of external elements and from the pathological reactions due to aging. In the case of paintings, the processes of deterioration can occur over comparatively short periods, even though the paints were prepared from modern chemical products, which presumably are able to challenge eternity better than the antique mixtures of pigments and natural substances.

The reaction of painted surfaces to light, atmospherical conditions, and the passing of the years occurs also on recent works of art. This calls for the need to control the reactions and to plan cleaning and maintenance operations thus limiting the chemical and physical changes brought about by time.

A particular analytical investigation regarding some contemporary paintings is being carried out in Paris by the Laboratoire de Recherche des Musées de France. This experiment which makes use of advanced instrumental technologies, examines a few paintings by Pablo Picasso as well as others.

There is no need to wait for centuries in order to appreciate that the works of Picasso must be preserved as one of the most striking testimonies of our century. In the ninety-two years of his life (from 1881 to 1973) he played the part of the leading man and interpreter of a restless and lacerated epoch driven mad by the destructive impulses that had so many times permeated it. An analysis of the period from the end of the 19th century to the mid-20th century is extremely complex. Amidst

FRANCE

revolutions and wars, radical alterations in the political geography of the continent and the reassertion of national identities; amidst trenches, concentration camps and bombings; between the "twilight" school of poetry and the theory of the "super-man"; between industrial empires and the proletariate; amongst "avant-garde" movements and psychoanalysis; and during a period of enlightening cultural and scientific experiences the path of the decades behind us is tortuous and also decisive in the identification of modern man's personality. During these decades, the intellectual world produced such provocative ideas that they disrupted entire ethical and aesthetical values of 19th century theories and burst out in an entirely new way of thinking. Pablo Picasso was a key figure in this contradictory and many-sided process which gave rise to modern Europe and a general change in society all over the world. His creative and poetical ability was vehement but always clear. The forceful, even brutal impulse of his paintings and of his images (deformed by those expressive demands) were pressing for bold exploration in all fields of art. The provocative display in some of his paintings, of the hidden monstrosities which lie in the unconscious mind along with the tenderness and joy of living which effuse from other paintings coupled with the severity of his brush strokes, permit no place for hesitation or self-contempt. These are only some features of his passionate and unprejudiced personality which permeated all aspects of his public and private life, in politics and towards his friends, his lovers and his enemies.

He was a man in the front row both in artistic experience and in his social activity. One can enthusiastically be for him or drastically be against him; indifference is not possible. An "expert" could certainly venture into debating whether the whole of Picasso's work, or just a part of it, will remain to express the emotions and the universal values of art. Whatever the verdict, future generations will inherit a highly representative testimony of a certain world and of its history. For example this is the case with the works which belong to the series of "Seated Women" painted from 1941 onwards during the Nazi occupation of France. The series is based upon the female portrait, a traditional subject of all time in painting. It became the expressive medium of that monstrous power that rampaged Europe at the time, defacing both the values and appearance of humanity. The "Seated Women" are not monsters blasted out from a nightmare or from the depths of a distorted personality. They are the personification of a certain reality, the symbol of the ferocity of a historical period, the picture of the agony caused to the most elementary human dignities, born of violence and of extermination.

78

P. Picasso, *Guernica*.

P. Picasso, *Massacre in Korea*.

79

80   P. Picasso, *Seated Woman* (1920).

In other paintings by Picasso – such as "Guernica" and "Massacre in Korea" – war is presented directly. In the "Seated Women" war is not faced directly, nevertheless the dramatic testimony of the impact of war on human life deeply touches our hearts and minds. As Picasso himself used to say, a painter has to be "constantly careful in the face of harrowing, passionate or gentle events of the world and adapt himself to fit in with such situations". In other words a painter has to stay close to reality. Only by total involvement in life he will be able to narrate it. Sometimes ideas and attributes are tied to ideology or moral considerations and other external circumstances. An artist may, in certain cases, decide to try out new styles and techniques to express his ideas and emotions. It is one of the tasks of art historians to judge them according to historical, logical and cultural criteria. Accordingly, even Picasso, the father of "synthetic cubism", finds a place in the history of art as one of those masters who revolutioned the rules and styles of painting. What however cannot be framed in historical schemes, is the boundless spiritual energy materialized in the man and transmitted to his art. Picasso is already somewhat of a myth and stands beyond our capacity to judge. He is no longer a personality who belongs to a certain period. He is an artist who filled on his own the world to which he belonged. He is one of those figures that rise like a giant in the boundless picture of life. He was a man who knew how to leave his enormous and profound mark on the collective memory of mankind.

82   Masolino, *The Original Sin*.

THE BRANCACCI CHAPEL
FROM THE GARDEN OF EDEN
INTO THE WORLD
A HOPE: TO RETURN

There was a time when mankind was happy and lived free from fear and shame, free from grief and hate. But a sin was committed which upset this harmony. It forced men and women to imbark on a weary and long journey through history. Adam and Eve are the symbols of free will and responsibility, of the power of temptation and passion, and after their fall, of the relentless punishment of the Final Judgement. A fall from the original condition of bliss and harmony down into the abyss. The human being is commanded to distinguish between good and evil and to conscientiously seek a salvation for reconciliation of his natural state and his divine origin.

From that very moment of the original sin, the cycle of events of man outside the gates of the Garden of Eden begins, and starts his perennial conflict between reality and the fading memories of lost happiness. This is an originary sin and on the stage of the Time appear various men and women, guilty but bent on living and struggling step by step to give over themselves. The destination of the journey is earthly death with victory over physical existence and then eternal salvation.

The myth of Adam and Eve, in all its variations, belongs to the collective conscience (lucid and submerged) of many different civilizations. It constitutes one of the most complex archetype which under certain aspects, still remains unfathomable. Amongst its representations in western Christian tradition, and one of the most famous from an artistical and intellectual point of view, is that preserved in Florence in the Church of the Carmine, on the walls of the Brancacci Chapel. Here is to be found a series of frescoes, some of the most famous of the Renaissance, painted by Masolino and Masaccio between 1424 and 1427. The series comprises the two paintings "The Original Sin", by Masolino and "The Banishment from the Earthly Paradise", by Masaccio. These two works are so different that they symbolically mark a turning point in art history. The first is the expression of an artistic movement known as International Gothic, which although cul-

ITALY

tured and refined, was inadequate to face up to Renaissance conceptions and their theories on mankind. The second painting expresses the revolutionary impulse of these new conceptions, from which Humanism of the 15th century and the culture of the 16th century developed. The whole work of Masaccio is regarded as a fundamental step in the history of art, both for its formal aspect and its meaning, and equals that of Giotto.

In this fresco Masolino tells us of the idyllic condition of a man and a woman living in a state of grace and favour, while, behind them is rising the menacing shadow of insidious temptation. Although beautiful, harmonious and naturally peaceful, the two seem in some way to be distracted and motionless as if they were too perfect to be true.

Perhaps this impression is due to the contrast with the scene painted by Masaccio where Adam and Eve have just experienced the first symbolical awareness of the negative content of a deed, such as temptation, deceit, conceit, in short the quintessence of sin. They have just crossed the threshold of Eden and approach the same world in which we live. Their bodies have lost their tall, slender elegance and a crude light falls over them. Adam hides his face, while Eve's face is reduced to a tragic mask. Her distorted expression makes it identical to any other woman's face distraught with anguish and displaying a terrifying image of earthly sorrow.

Masaccio doesn't confine himself to represent only the idea of the "Banishment". He tells us clearly that this is the first step of all humanity which is distressed but cannot turn back with shoulders bent under the weight of guilt and responsibility, but strong in the unyielding motion of its body. The Avenging Angel with a gesture shows the way out of Eden and into reality and history, where the man and the woman will be given the energy to play their roles.

The restoration of the Brancacci Chapel, initiated in 1984 by the Soprintendenza ai Beni Artistici e Storici of Florence, challenged the team of technicians to rediscover the emotive potential of the frescoes by restoring their original beauty.

Soon the public will be able to share the expressive power of these masterpieces of Italian art. The operation required a considerable series of preliminary chemical and physical tests along with well-conceived plans about how to carry out the practical phases of the restoration.

Amongst these, one in particular attracted public attention. Between the 17th and the 18th century both the paintings of Adam and Eve were judged somewhat too "naturalistic". These nudes had never disturbed the contemporaries of Masolino and Masaccio. However, centuries later when sensitivity towards the human body had become

"...behind them is rising the menacing shadow of insidious temptation."

distorted and malicious and had even affected attitudes towards the works of art, the nudes became a source of irritation. Therefore, probably by order of the Carmelitan friars who had dedicated the church to the Virgin, some leafy branches were added in watercolour (thereby also "inventing" an arboreal species which is non-existant). The leaves were strategically placed to "clothe" certain parts of the bodies. These additions were unfortunately in total discord with the balance and light of the frescoes. It also seems that deprived of its full meaning, the gesture of Eve who strives to hide her body, fails to explain how modesty about nudity arose for the first time.

After the removal of these additions, the paint of the frescoes

86   Masaccio, *The Banishment
          from the Earthly Paradise*.

"Adam hides his face, while Eve's face is reduced to a tragic mask. Her distorted expression makes it identical to any other woman's face distraught with anguish and displaying a terrifying image of earthly sorrow."

required lengthy work of cleaning. The soot from candles, atmospheric pollution and time had darkened and dulled the colours. Also a coat of some kind of substance had been spread on the paintings to protect them. The result was that they suffered further damage and the coating had to be removed with a special procedure in order not to take away the underlying colours. The frescoes of the Brancacci Chapel are now back to their splendour, to the brightness originally created by Masolino and Masaccio. And thanks to the extraordinary methods of conservation used purposely for the surrounding environment, they will preserve their stories and their message for a long time to come.

Perhaps one day someone may paint the last chapter of the story. It would show a man and a woman in the act of abandoning their clothes and their sorrows to return to their original abode through the same gate from which they were banished with their faces smiling but well aware of their experience. They will be the Adam and Eve of the future, eventually readmitted into Eden, progenitors of a third mankind. Here they will be strong and beautiful, with the maturity and vital energy of those who, at the end of a thousand-year journey, are the creators of happiness both for themselves and for future generations.

The use of Perkin-Elmer instruments in studies on restoration and preservation of works of art and archaeological discoveries

It is maintained these days, that a large percentage of the work of restoration of paintings is carried out to remedy the damage caused by interventions of cleaning, preservation and repairs undertaken in the past. Therefore, over and above the wear and tear of time, natural calamities such as fire, collapsed buildings, and those caused by vandalism, the most serious threat to our artistic inheritance has come from the action undertaken to ensure their maintenance and care.

At the entrance of the Opificio delle Pietre Dure in Florence, which is one of the most important centers of restoration in Europe, one can read an inscription taken from what is considered to be the first comprehensive treatise on restoration, the "Manuale ragionato per la parte meccanica dell'arte del ristauratore dei dipinti" (A commented manual for the mechanical processes in the art of restoring paintings). It was written in 1866 by Count Giovanni Secco Suardo, and reads: "If you question history, or ask for the opinion of an art specialist and examine those objects which are left to us, you will have to admit absolutely that it was neither time, nor war, nor fires, nor iconoclasts that destroyed the greater number of paintings, but the presumptuous ignorance of those who thought they could clean them." The situation today is completely changed. Each work of restoration is based on an extensive and detailed approach towards the works of art and their environment, with an historical, artistic and scientific study prior to any intervention. The modern conception of restoration no longer leaves room for improvisation and approximation. On the contrary, it follows technical and cultural progress and programs.

In this context, a role of utmost importance is played by those instruments of modern technology which the analyst and the chemist or the physicist, rely upon in the salient steps in the restoration work. Among such instruments, those produced by Perkin-Elmer are of great relevance and are employed by the restoration teams of the most important Institutes and Organizations in Europe and in all other parts of the world. Let us, therefore, take a quick look at methods of instrumental analysis, knowing full well that in line with the aims of this book, we must limit ourselves to quoting only part of the most interesting applications.

We therefore apologize in advance, to those who, though authors of important works, are not mentioned in the brief notes which follow.

89

Objectively however, we are compelled to remember that not everything that was done in the past is to be forgotten. The report on an analysis which follows gives an example.

"The paint appears to be free from mercury (Vermilion), antimony (Antimony red), chrome (Chrome red), sulphates (Venetian red), while a certain quantity of iron was found. All other tests carried out to seek the presence of lacquer (trying to obtain a solution in alcohol, diluted hydrochloric acid and ammonia, and trying to dye vegetable and animal fibers) had negative results. It must therefore be concluded that the pigmentation is exclusively due to red ochre. This conclusion is confirmed also by the fact that having repeatedly treated the pigment in question with diluted hydrochloric acid, there was no fading of the tone of the colour, as evidently the colour is due only to iron oxide which is not soluble in hydrochloric acid."

This passage was taken from the report of an analysis carried out by Vincenzo Sica in 1938 on samples of paint taken from the ceiling of the Sistine Chapel, with a view to identifying the pigments used by Michelangelo. It gives an idea of the limits of the analytical methods available in a past which is only 50 years ago! As is evident from the report, it was possible to arrive at a conclusion only by exclusion. Notwithstanding this, the majority of the results have been demonstrated to be exact. Confirmation came from data provided by a Perkin-Elmer atomic absorption spectrophotometer which for several years has been used by the Cabinet for Scientific Research of the Vatican Museums. With this instrument it is possible today to obtain information in a much more rapid and accurate manner, in order to define with precision the "palette" used by Michelangelo and to recognize the different pigments that had been used for restoration and repainting in the centuries which followed.

Infrared spectroscopy

This technique can be very widely employed in the field of works of art as it permits an accurate identification of substances which range from binders to pigments, from paints to waxes, from resins to lacquers. Furthermore it can be also used on inorganic and stone material. Fundamental questions in the study of works of art have found an answer in the analyses carried out by means of Perkin-Elmer IR spectrophotometers. Research on El-Fayum portraits, for instance, led to the identification of the peculiar nature of the wax used as a colour binder. For example, in order to make beeswax workable at a temperature lower than that of its melting point, it was subject to a treatment with soda or other basic salt drawn from Egyptian deposits thus obtaining a product known as "Punic wax".

In practice these instruments are employed to study all binders in paintings including synthetic polymers used by "modern" painters as is the case with the research being carried out on Picasso's paintings at the Louvre in Paris.

It is important to highlight the introduction, in the very recent years, of FT-IR spectrometers which provide a series of advantages which are most important in this field: even smaller samples, spectra acquired and processed by computer and microscope coupling which allows the realization of spectra on samples as small as 10 micrometers. A modern Perkin-Elmer FT-IR was employed for the restoration of "The meagre company" at the Rijksmuseum in Amsterdam. The use of infrared technique is also typical in investigations on fakes. A simple IR analysis allows for the unmistakably distinguishing of natural amber (a material which was used in the past to make refined objects) from even the most carefully produced imitations.

Ultraviolet/visible spectroscopy

One of the most famous cases of restoration of recent years is that of the series of frescoes of the Brancacci Chapel in Florence. A fundamental step in the operation was the research work which was carried out with a Perkin-Elmer UV-VIS spectrophotometer (which is equipped with an external integrating sphere) in use at the Istituto di Ricerca sulle Onde Elettromagnetiche of the CNR of Florence. The spectrophotometer was used to acquire and store in a computer, over one hundred reflected spectra from several areas of the frescoes. The external integrating sphere allows for working directly on the painting without damaging it. The spectrum is taken from a circular surface having a diameter of about 9 mm (about 1/3 of an inch) which is enough to ensure reliable averaged spectra, but not so wide as to include other colours.

The use of UV-VIS spectroscopy provided important data regarding both the characteristics of the original pigments and the different kind of substances that had to be removed in the various steps of the cleaning of the frescoes. Moreover, the colour spectra will remain available as extremely important data for the future. This is a feature that characterizes present day restoration. Complete and detailed documentation of the work undertaken is provided to allow whoever follows to operate with reliable data and with a full knowledge of the interventions that have taken place on works of art. UV-VIS spectroscopy is also widely used in the maintenance and restoration of stone and marble. In particular to control the effect of acid rain on these materials used for sculptures and architecture.

Atomic absorption spectroscopy

This is a further technique which, like infrared spectroscopy, has found wide application in restoration of works of art and in the study of archaeological exhibits. Atomic absorption provides selected data on the kind and amount of metal elements present in stonework, bronzes, and in the pigments of the stained-glass windows in cathedrals. Such instruments, for instance, are used in the Laboratorio de Investigaciones del Patrimonio Histórico Artístico de Castilla y León, which is part of the Escuela Técnica Superior de Ingenieros Industriales, at Valladolid in Spain. This laboratory focuses its interest on studies of the alterations which occur in the different kinds of stone which over the centuries created cathedrals, palaces, and monuments. (For instance the limestone and dolomite of Burgos cathedral, the sandstone of buildings in Salamanca, or again the calcareous standstone of the romanesque churches of

Segovia). Once the necessary operations of consolidation of the stone and protective treatment had been completed, the effectiveness of the interventions were checked by thermal analysis. Atomic absorption spectroscopy was also, as we have already mentioned, one of the main aspects of the fascinating research on the origin and dating of the Riace Bronzes. Through an exact knowledge of the composition of the alloy it allowed a reconstruction of a good number of the events, which supported by artistic and historical evidence, we believe represent the true history of the two statues.

A similar method was applied to the restoration of the Bronzes from Cartoceto. Once it was established that the bronze used in the casting had come from the same batch, the scientific hypothesis that the various fragments discovered all belonged to the same monument was confirmed.

This research was undertaken by the Restoration Center of the Soprintendenza ai Beni Archeologici of Tuscany.

Also in the restoration of the Sistine Chapel, as we have already seen, atomic absorption spectroscopy played a role of utmost importance. A Perkin-Elmer AA spectrophotometer is also installed in the laboratory of the National Museum of Thessalonike in Greece. Among the many research studies carried out there, a very significant one was done on the "Crater of Derveni", a precious archaeological exhibit and the only one of its kind, which dates back to 2400 years ago and was found during the excavations of Vergina.

To all appearances the crater (bowl) looks as if it was gilded. But in the age when it was made, such a technique was still unknown. The famous receptacle, however, was made of a special bronze alloy. The exact proportions of copper, tin, zinc and silver were revealed by analyses carried out on a series of micro-samples. The golden appearance has to be attributed to the high percentage of tin in the alloy. This peculiarity implied particular difficulties in the working of it. The unknown craftsman who forged the richly and finely decorated bowl must have possessed a masterly skill in order to transform such a "hostile" material into such a splendid and refined object that we still admire today.

Gas chromatography

Chemical analysis in the field of restoration are often faced with very complex situations. These occur, for instance, when the binding materials used in a painting are no longer soluble.

Restoration work carried out in the past often used "non-reversible" substances. Today's techniques of restoration use, whenever possible, materials that can be removed. In any case, both restorer and analyst are faced with a serious problem. First the removal of certain substances and secondly, their identification. The use of IR spectroscopy does not always offer a solution to this problem. At times it cannot be applied or it cannot provide conclusive answers. In such cases, gas chromatography combined with pyrolisis using extremely small samples weighing less than a milligram can be used. The principle on which it works is the same as the one which permitted the development of such technique in the industrial field and in the analysis of polymers. It offers valid assistance to restoration because of its rapid procedures and satisfactory results and above all by providing case studies of analyses carried out on appropriately prepared samples. Pyrolisis coupled with gas chromatography is successfully used for example, in the laboratories of the Louvre in Paris and in those of the Opificio delle Pietre Dure in Florence. Studies are being carried out to standardize, once and for all, the procedure. Practical experience is being gained concerning substances used as binders such as eggs, glues made of rabbit skin, casein and linseed oil and, for more recent paintings, one has to add synthetic polymers.

Liquid chromatography (HPLC)

It is known as "the broth" (beverone) the mixture applied to the vaulted ceiling of the Sistine Chapel in Rome in the course of the first restorations. This took place a few decades after the completion of the masterpiece. It was a concoction of organic substances which was applied with the praiseworthy intention of protecting Michelangelo's frescoes. In actual fact, as centuries went by, it was one of the causes of their turning brown. It was necessary to study its composition with the aid of various analytical techniques, among which was liquid chromatography (HPLC), in order to choose the most suitable way for its removal.

A Perkin-Elmer liquid chromatograph is also at the disposal of the restoration team of the Tudor flagship, the famous Mary Rose, in Great Britain. Here the instrument is used to monitor the stabilization and preservation treatment of the ship, a treatment based on solutions of polyethylene glycol of different molecular weight (200, 600, 1500, and 4000). In particular, the concentration of glycol adsorbed and retained by the wood is being determined, along with the various levels of penetration in relation to the molecular size.

During this work the liquid chromatograph is connected to a computer which allows for automatic registration of the distribution of the various portions of different molecular weight in the sample of wood being analyzed.

Thermal analysis

In the mid-sixties Perkin-Elmer built DSC-1, the first instrument of a line dedicated to thermal analysis. The DSC measures the amount of heat released or absorbed by a sample by means of such phenomena as fusion, solidification or variations of crystal structures. The instruments rapidly progressed, first into research on plastic materials, then into the pharmaceutical industry. In the field of restoration this technique is employed more and more frequently. It is used by the researchers of Birbeck College in London in the studies on great English Masters such as Thomas Gainsborough and John Constable. The object of the research concerns the binders used by the artists and how the passing of time has affected them.

Another interesting application of DSC is in the preservation of ancient leather bindings and text written on parchments by the Centre de Recherches sur la Conservation des Documents Graphiques of Paris. Using differential calorimetry, the reaction of proteinous substances to preservative treatments

93

is studied, especially of collagen which softens skins and leathers and makes them supple. A typical alteration that is noticed with this kind of compounds is denaturation which is an irreversible reaction which causes the material to harden and crack. DSC is able to study this phenomenon which occurs with heat absorption. It was therefore possible to set up treatments with suitable chemical substances which make leather supple and soft again and ensure its perfect preservation throughout the years.

In the field of thermal analysis other than differential calorimetry, another important analytical technique is thermogravimetry, which is based upon measuring the loss of weight of samples due to rises in temperature. The TGA instrument operates on micro-quantities of substances and indicates with great accuracy both the temperature at which release of material takes place and the corresponding loss in weight. Applications generally concern all those materials which have undergone baking. The role played by TGA in the artistic field is evident, both in restoration planning and in the discovery of forgeries. Experience on Etruscan vases is symbolic. Especially in the last century, it often happened, that after an archaeological discovery of broken pottery (usually as part of funeral accessories) the restorers' enthusiasm lead them to rebuild broken vases with fragments belonging to different ones. The error justified, in the past, by the similarity of colour, shape and design, is today detectable by submitting micro-quantities of the fragments to a thermogravimetric analysis. This accurately determines the temperature at which the "baking" of the material was carried out. It is most unlikely that the means available to Etruscan ceramists would allow the baking of all their vases exactly at the same temperature. The analysis then provide data which permit identification of the fragments which come from the same baking operation. Thus, research can be carried out to identify forgeries produced in more recent times, using processes which are inevitably different from the ancient ones.

94

CONTENTS

Photographic Credits